The Ford Distinguished Lectures . . . Vol. III

Books by Herbert A. Simon

NEW SCIENCE OF MANAGEMENT DECISION

ORGANIZATIONS (with J. G. March)

MODELS OF MAN

CENTRALIZATION VS DECENTRALIZATION IN ORGANIZING THE CONTROLLER'S DEPARTMENT (with Kozmetsky, Guetzkow, and Tyndall)

PUBLIC ADMINISTRATION (with Smithburg and Thompson)

ADMINISTRATIVE BEHAVIOR

TECHNIQUE OF MUNICIPAL ADMINISTRATION (with others)

MEASURING MUNICIPAL ACTIVITIES (with C. E. Ridley)

The New Science
of Management
Decision

by

Herbert A. Simon

Professor of Administration; Graduate School of Industrial

Administration; Carnegie Institute of Technology

and Ford Distinguished Visiting Professor; School of Commerce,

Accounts, and Finance; New York University

HARPER & ROW, PUBLISHERS
New York and Evanston

Printed by:
American Book–Stratford Press, Inc.
Library of Congress catalog card number: 60-15199

TO

Kathie, Pete, and Barb

Whose world it will be.

Contents

Foreword   ix

    THOMAS L. NORTON, Dean

Preface   xi

The Executive as Decision Maker   1

Traditional Decision-Making Methods   9

New Techniques for Programmed Decision Making   14
    Lecture I——March 24, 1960

Heuristic Problem Solving   21
    Lecture II——March 31, 1960

Organizational Design: Man-Machine Systems for Decision   35
    Making
        Lecture III——April 7, 1960

Foreword

THOMAS L. NORTON, Dean
School of Commerce, Accounts, and Finance
New York University

THE School of Commerce, Accounts, and Finance was singularly honored to have as Ford Distinguished Visiting Professor for 1960 Dr. Herbert A. Simon. This eminent social scientist delivered the third series of public lectures, which were held on March 24, 31, and April 7. These addresses, as well as the previous series by Sir Noel Hall and Ordway Tead, were made possible through a grant from the Ford Foundation. This grant established the Ford Distinguished Visiting Professorship and is designed to bring to the School of Commerce outstanding educators from American and overseas universities.

Educated at the University of Chicago, Dr. Simon has been a member of the faculties of the University of California (Berkeley), Illinois Institute of Technology, and, since 1949, the Carnegie Institute of Technology, where he now serves as Associate Dean of the Graduate School of Industrial Administration and Professor of Administration. He is a consultant to government and business organizations, a director-at-large of the Social Science Research Council, and a director of the Nuclear Science and Engineering Corporation.

Dr. Simon, a member of both Phi Beta Kappa and Sigma Xi, is the author or co-author of nearly 200 books and research papers in organizational theory and related areas of the behavioral sciences. His books include *Administrative Behavior, Public Administration, Models of Man,* and *Organizations.*

During the last five years, Dr. Simon and his colleagues have been engaged in fundamental research on the processes of decision making, using electronic computers to simulate human thinking. In these lectures he discusses some of the results of this research and the future consequences for American business. Not only does he cite the types of business problems which can be handled successfully at the present time by automated processes, but he also describes some current scientific investigations into the possibilities of automating non-repetitive types of decisions. These pioneering investigations on this frontier of knowledge give us glimpses of what to expect in the future when a business firm is confronted with such questions as— "Should we build a new plant?" "Where should it be located?" "Should a new product be introduced?" "Should an old one be discontinued?"

Dr. Simon also explores—in terms of organizational structure, employment opportunities, work satisfaction, and creativity—what the nature of business will be as these changes in methods of business decision making take place.

A new type of industrial revolution is on the horizon and we are honored to give Dr. Simon the opportunity to present his picture of this business world of the future.

Preface

My research activities during the past decade have brought me into contact with developments in the use of electronic digital computers. These computers are startling even in a world that takes atomic energy and the prospects of space travel in its stride. The computer and the new decision-making techniques associated with it are bringing changes in white-collar, executive, and professional work as momentous as those the introduction of machinery has brought to manual jobs.

The invitation extended to me by the School of Commerce, Accounts, and Finance of New York University, to spend some weeks there as Ford Distinguished Visiting Professor and to deliver a series of public lectures, provided me a welcome opportunity to reflect about the organizational and social implications of these rapid technical developments. The lectures, slightly expanded here from the form of their public presentation, record the product—a very speculative product—of my reflections.

I do not apologize for extrapolating beyond our present certain knowledge. In our kind of world, those who are closest to important new technical innovations have a responsibility to provide reasoned interpretations of these innovations and their significance. Such interpretations should be, of course, the beginning and not the end of public discussion. But they cannot be made at all without extrapolation from present certainties into future probabilities.

In this printed version, three lectures have become five chapters. The three distinct subtopics that were covered in the first lecture constitute the first three chapters; Chapter IV corresponds to the second lecture; and Chapter V to the third.

I have acknowledged at several points in the text my debt to the colleagues who have been my partners in research in this area—and particularly to Allen Newell. My debts go far beyond these specific acknowledgments—how far I cannot specify without implicating my

friends in conclusions with which they might wish to disagree. I want
also to thank Dean Norton and his associates at New York University,
for the opportunity to present the lectures and to discuss their content
with them. Finally, I am especially grateful to my wife, whose advice
and comment on succeeding drafts of the manuscript have very much
improved the style and content, and who also undertook the final
editing.

Herbert A. Simon

May, 1960

The New Science of Management Decision

The Executive

as Decision Maker

WHAT part does decision making play in managing? I shall find it convenient to take mild liberties with the English language by using "decision making" as though it were synonymous with "managing."

What is our mental image of a decision maker? Is he a brooding man on horseback who suddenly rouses himself from thought and issues an order to a subordinate? Is he a happy-go-lucky fellow, a coin poised on his thumbnail, ready to risk his action on the toss? Is he an alert, gray-haired businessman, sitting at the board of directors' table with his associates, caught at the moment of saying "aye" or "nay"? Is he a bespectacled gentleman, bent over a docket of papers, his pen hovering over the line marked (X)?

All of these images have a significant point in common. In them, the decision maker is a man at the moment of choice, ready to plant his foot on one or another of the routes that lead from the crossroads. All the images falsify decision by focusing on its final moment. All of them ignore the whole lengthy, complex process of alerting, exploring, and analysing that precede that final moment.

INTELLIGENCE, DESIGN, AND CHOICE IN DECISION MAKING

In treating decision making as synonymous with managing, I shall be referring not merely to the final act of choice among alternatives, but rather to the whole process of decision. Decision making comprises three principal phases: finding occasions for making a decision; finding possible courses of action; and choosing among courses of action. These three activities account for quite different fractions of the time budgets of executives. The fractions vary greatly from one organization level to another and from one executive to another, but we can make some generalizations about them even from casual

1

observation. Executives spend a large fraction of their time surveying the economic, technical, political, and social environment to identify new conditions that call for new actions. They probably spend an even larger fraction of their time, individually or with their associates, seeking to invent, design, and develop possible courses of action for handling situations where a decision is needed. They spend a small fraction of their time in choosing among alternative actions already developed to meet an identified problem and already analysed for their consequences. The three fractions, added together, account for most of what executives do.[1]

The first phase of the decision-making process—searching the environment for conditions calling for decision—I shall call *intelligence* activity (borrowing the military meaning of intelligence). The second phase—inventing, developing, and analysing possible courses of action—I shall call *design* activity. The third phase—selecting a particular course of action from those available—I shall call *choice* activity.

Let me illustrate these three phases of decision. In the past five years, many companies have reorganized their accounting and other data processing activities in order to make use of large electronic computers. How has this come about? Computers first became available commercially in the early 1950s. Although, in some vague and general sense, company managements were aware that computers existed, few managements had investigated their possible applications with any thoroughness before about 1955. For most companies, the use of computers required no decision before that time because it hadn't been placed on the agenda.[2]

The intelligence activity preceding the introduction of computers tended to come about in one of two ways. Some companies—for example, in the aircraft and atomic energy industries—were burdened with enormously complex computations for engineering design. Because efficiency in computation was a constant problem, and because the design departments were staffed with engineers who could understand, at least in general, the technology of computers, awareness of computers and their potentialities came early to these companies.

---

[1] The way in which these activities take shape within an organization is described in some detail in James G. March and Herbert A. Simon, *Organizations* (New York: John Wiley & Sons, Inc., 1958), chaps. 6 and 7.

[2] Richard M. Cyert, Herbert A. Simon, and Donald B. Trow, "Observation of a Business Decision," *Journal of Business,* vol. 29 (1956), pp. 237-248.

After computers were already in extensive use for design calculations, businesses with a large number-processing load—insurance companies, accounting departments in large firms, banks—discovered these new devices and began to consider seriously their introduction.

Once it was recognized that computers might have a place in modern business, a major design task had to be carried out in each company before they could be introduced. It is now a commonplace that payrolls can be prepared by computers. Programs in both the general and computer senses for doing this are relatively easy to design in any given situation.[3] To develop the first computer programs for preparing payroll, however, was a major research and development project. Few companies having carried their investigations of computers to the point where they had definite plans for their use, failed to install them. Commitment to the new course of action took place gradually as the intelligence and design phases of the decision were going on. The final choice was, in many instances, almost *pro forma*.

Generally speaking, intelligence activity precedes design, and design activity precedes choice. The cycle of phases is, however, far more complex than this sequence suggests. Each phase in making a particular decision is itself a complex decision-making process. The design phase, for example, may call for new intelligence activities; problems at any given level generate subproblems that, in turn, have their intelligence, design, and choice phases, and so on. There are wheels within wheels within wheels. Nevertheless, the three large phases are often clearly discernible as the organizational decision process unfolds. They are closely related to the stages in problem solving first described by John Dewey:

What is the problem?

What are the alternatives?

Which alternative is best?[4]

It may be objected that I have ignored the task of carrying out decisions. I shall merely observe by the way that seeing that decisions are executed is again decision-making activity. A broad policy decision creates a new condition for the organization's executives that

[3] For a good discussion on the use of the computer for such purposes, see Robert H. Gregory and Richard L. Van Horn, *Automatic Data-Processing Systems* (San Francisco: Wadsworth Publishing Company, Inc., 1960).

[4] John Dewey, *How We Think* (New York: D. C. Heath & Company, 1910), chap. 8.

calls for the design and choice of a course of action for executing the policy. Executing policy, then, is indistinguishable from making more detailed policy. For this reason, I shall feel justified in taking my pattern for decision making as a paradigm for most executive activity.

DEVELOPING DECISION-MAKING SKILLS

It is an obvious step from the premise that managing is decision making to the conclusion that the important skills for an executive are decision-making skills. It is generally believed that good decision makers, like good athletes, are born, not made. The belief is about as true in the one case as it is in the other.

That human beings come into the world endowed unequally with biological potential for athletic prowess is undeniable. They also come endowed unequally with intelligence, cheerfulness, and many other characteristics and potentialities. To a limited extent, we can measure some aspects of that endowment—height, weight, perhaps intelligence. Whenever we make such measurements and compare them with adult performance, we obtain significant, but low, correlations. A man who is not a natural athlete is unlikely to run the four-minute mile; but many men who are natural athletes have never come close to that goal. A man who is not "naturally" intelligent is unlikely to star in science; but many intelligent scientists are not stars.

A good athlete is born when a man with some natural endowment, by dint of practice, learning, and experience develops that natural endowment into a mature skill. A good executive is born when a man with some natural endowment (intelligence and some capacity for interacting with his fellow men) by dint of practice, learning, and experience develops his endowment into a mature skill. The skills involved in intelligence, design, and choosing activities are as learnable and trainable as the skills involved in driving, recovering, and putting a golf ball. I hope to indicate some of the things a modern executive needs to learn about decision making.

EXECUTIVE RESPONSIBILITY FOR ORGANIZATIONAL DECISION MAKING

The executive's job involves not only making decisions himself, but also seeing that the organization, or part of an organization, that he directs makes decisions effectively. The vast bulk of the decision-making activity for which he is responsible is not his personal activity, but the activity of his subordinates.

Nowadays, with the advent of computers, we can think of information as something almost tangible; strings of symbols which, like strips of steel or plastic ribbons, can be processed—changed from one form to another. We can think of white-collar organizations as factories for processing information. The executive is the factory manager, with all the usual responsibilities for maintaining the factory operation, getting it back into operation when it breaks down, and proposing and carrying through improvements in its design.

There is no reason to expect that a man who has acquired a fairly high level of personal skill in decision-making activity will have a correspondingly high skill in designing efficient decision-making systems. To imagine that there is such a connection is like supposing that a man who is a good weight lifter can therefore design cranes. The skills of designing and maintaining the modern decision-making systems we call organizations are less intuitive skills. Hence, they are even more susceptible to training than the skills of personal decision making.

PROGRAMMED AND NONPROGRAMMED DECISIONS

In discussing how executives now make decisions, and how they will make them in the future, let us distinguish two polar types of decisions. I shall call them *programmed decisions* and *nonprogrammed decisions,* respectively. Having christened them, I hasten to add that they are not really distinct types, but a whole continuum, with highly programmed decisions at one end of that continuum and highly unprogrammed decisions at the other end. We can find decisions of all shades of gray along the continuum, and I use the terms programmed and nonprogrammed simply as labels for the black and the white of the range.[5]

Decisions are programmed to the extent that they are repetitive and routine, to the extent that a definite procedure has been worked out for handling them so that they don't have to be treated *de novo*

[5] See March and Simon, *op. cit.,* pp. 139-142 and 177-180 for further discussion of these types of decisions. The labels used there are slightly different.

each time they occur. The obvious reason why programmed decisions tend to be repetitive, and vice versa, is that if a particular problem recurs often enough, a routine procedure will usually be worked out for solving it. Numerous examples of programmed decisions in organizations will occur to you: pricing ordinary customers' orders; determining salary payments to employees who have been ill; reordering office supplies.

Decisions are nonprogrammed to the extent that they are novel, unstructured, and consequential. There is no cut-and-dried method for handling the problem because it hasn't arisen before, or because its precise nature and structure are elusive or complex, or because it is so important that it deserves a custom-tailored treatment. General Eisenhower's D-Day decision is a good example of a nonprogrammed decision. Remember, we are considering not merely the final act of ordering the attack, but the whole complex of intelligence and design activities that preceded it. Many of the components of the decisions were programmed—by standard techniques for military planning—but before these components could be designed they had to be provided with a broader framework of military and political policy.

I have borrowed the term program from the computer trade, and intend it in the sense in which it is used there. A *program* is a detailed prescription or strategy that governs the sequence of responses of a system to a complex task environment. Most of the programs that govern organizational response are not as detailed or as precise as computer programs. However, they all have the same intent: to permit an adaptive response of the system to the situation.

In what sense, then, can we say that the response of a system to a situation is nonprogrammed? Surely something determines the response. That something, that collection of rules of procedure, is by definition a program. By nonprogrammed I mean a response where the system has no specific procedures to deal with situations like the one at hand, but must fall back on whatever *general* capacity it has for intelligent, adaptive, problem-oriented action. In addition to his specific skills and specific knowledge, man has some general problem-solving capacities. Given almost any kind of situation, no matter how novel or perplexing, he can begin to reason about it in terms of ends and means.

This general problem-solving equipment is not always effective.

Men often fail to solve problems, or they reach unsatisfactory solutions. But man is seldom completely helpless in a new situation. He possesses general problem-solving equipment which, however inefficient, fills some of the gaps in his special problem-solving skills. And organizations, as collections of men, have some of this same general adaptive capacity.

The cost of using general-purpose programs to solve problems is usually high. It is advantageous to reserve these programs for situations that are truly novel, where no alternative programs are available. If any particular class of situations recurs often enough, a special-purpose program can be developed which gives better solutions and gives them more cheaply than the general problem-solving apparatus.

My reason for distinguishing between programmed and nonprogrammed decisions is that different techniques are used for handling the programmed and the nonprogrammed aspects of our decision making. The distinction, then, will be a convenient one for classifying these techniques. I shall use it for that purpose, hoping that the reader will remind himself from time to time that the world is mostly gray with only a few spots of pure black or white.

The four-fold table below will provide a map of the territory I propose to cover. In the northern half of the map are some techniques related to programmed decision making, in the southern half, some techniques related to nonprogrammed decision making. In the western half of the map I placed the classical techniques used in decision making—the kit of tools that has been used by executives and organizations from the time of the earliest recorded history up to the present generation. In the eastern half of the map I placed the new techniques of decision making—tools that have been forged largely since World War II, and that are only now coming into extensive use in management in this country. I shall proceed across the map from west to east, and from north to south, taking up, in order, the north-west and the south-west quadrants (chapter II), the north-east quadrant (chapter III), and the south-east quadrant (chapter IV).

I can warn you now to what conclusion this journey is going to lead. We are in the midst of a major revolution in the art or science —whichever you prefer to call it—of management and organization. I shall try to describe the nature of this revolution and, in my final chapter, to discuss its implications.

FIGURE 1.   TRADITIONAL AND MODERN TECHNIQUES OF DECISION MAKING

TYPES OF DECISIONS	DECISION-MAKING TECHNIQUES	
	Traditional	*Modern*

Programmed:
 	
Routine, repetitive decisions
Organization develops specific processes for handling them
	1. Habit
	2. Clerical routine:
	   Standard operating procedures
	3. Organization structure:
	   Common expectations
	   A system of subgoals
	   Well-defined informational channels
		1. Operations Research:
		   Mathematical analysis
		   Models
		   Computer simulation
		2. Electronic data processing

Nonprogrammed:
 	
One-shot, ill-structured novel, policy decisions
Handled by general problem-solving processes
	1. Judgment, intuition, and creativity
	2. Rules of thumb
	3. Selection and training of executives
		Heuristic problem-solving techniques applied to:
		   (a) training human decision makers
		   (b) constructing heuristic computer programs

Traditional

Decision-Making Methods

Lᴇᴛ us examine the western half of our map of decision-making techniques (Fig. I). This half represents methods that have been widely understood and applied in human organizations at least from the time of the building of the pyramids. In painting with a broad brush, I may convey the impression that there was no progress in organizational matters during the course of three millennia. I do not believe this to be true, and I do not intend to imply it. But the progress that was made did not enlarge the repertory of basic mechanisms to which I shall refer.

We shall consider, in turn, techniques for making programmed decisions and techniques for making nonprogrammed decisions.

TRADITIONAL TECHNIQUES FOR PROGRAMMED DECISIONS

"Man," says William James, "is born with a tendency to do more things than he has ready-made arrangements for in his nerve centres. Most of the performances of other animals are automatic. But in him the number of them is so enormous, that most of them must be the fruit of painful study. If practice did not make perfect, nor habit economize the expense of nervous and muscular energy, he would therefore be in a sorry plight."[1]

Habit is the most general, the most pervasive, of all techniques for making programmed decisions. The collective memories of organization members are vast encyclopedias of factual knowledge, habitual skills, and operating procedures. The large costs associated with bringing new members into organizations are principally costs of providing the new members, through formal training and experience, with the

[1] William James, *The Principles of Psychology* (New York: Henry Holt & Company, 1890) or (New York: Dover Publications, Inc., 1950), vol. 1, p. 113.

repertoire of skills and other habits they need in their jobs. Partly, the organization provides these habits; partly, it acquires them by selecting new employees who have already learned them in the educational and training institutions that society maintains.

Closely related to habits are standard operating procedures. The only difference between habits and standard operating procedures is that the former have become internalized—recorded in the central nervous system—while the latter begin as formal, written, recorded programs. Standard operating procedures provide a means for indoctrinating new members into the habitual patterns of organizational behavior, a means for reminding old members of patterns that any one member uses so infrequently that they never become completely habitual, and a means for bringing habitual patterns out into the open where they can be examined, modified, and improved.

Organization structure, over and above standard operating procedures, is itself a partial specification of decision-making programs. The organization structure establishes a common set of presuppositions and expectations as to which members of the organization are responsible for which classes of decisions; it establishes a structure of subgoals to serve as criteria of choice in various parts of the organization; and it establishes intelligence responsibilities in particular organization units for scrutinizing specific parts of the organization's environment and for communicating events requiring attention to appropriate decision points.

In the past, the improvement of programmed decision making in organizations has focused largely upon these techniques: upon improving the knowledge, skills, and habits of individual employees by means of training programs and planned tours of duty; upon developing better standard operating procedures and securing adherence to them; and upon modifying the structure of the organization itself, the division of labor, the subgoal structure, the allocation of responsibilities.

Mankind has possessed for many centuries an impressive collection of techniques for developing and maintaining predictable programmed responses in an organization to those problems posed by its environment that are relatively repetitive and well-structured. The history of the development of these techniques has never been written—much of it is undoubtedly buried in prehistory—but one can point to particular periods of innovation. The scientific management movement, and particularly the development of standard methods for performing repetitive work, is one of the most recent of these.

TRADITIONAL TECHNIQUES FOR NONPROGRAMMED DECISIONS

When we turn to the area of nonprogrammed decisions, we have much less to point to in the way of specific, describable techniques. When we ask how executives in organizations make nonprogrammed decisions, we are generally told that they "exercise judgment," and that this judgment depends, in some undefined way, upon experience, insight, and intuition. If the decision we are inquiring about was a particularly difficult one, or one that yielded especially impressive results, we may be told that creativity was required.

There is a scene in *Le Malade Imaginaire* in which the physician is asked why opium puts people to sleep. "Because it possesses a dormitive faculty," he replies triumphantly. To name a phenomenon is not to explain it. Saying that nonprogrammed decisions are made by exercising judgment *names* that phenomenon but does not explain it. It doesn't help the man who lacks judgment (i.e., who doesn't make decisions well) to acquire it.

Making programmed decisions depends on relatively simple psychological processes that are somewhat understood, at least at the practical level. These include habit, memory, simple manipulations of things and symbols. Making nonprogrammed decisions depends on psychological processes that, until recently, have not been understood at all. Because we have not understood them, our theories about nonprogrammed decision making have been rather empty and our practical advice only moderately helpful.

One thing we have known about nonprogrammed decision making is that it can be improved somewhat by training in orderly thinking. In addition to the very specific habits one can acquire for doing very specific things, one can acquire the habit—when confronted with a vague and difficult situation—of asking, "What is the problem?" We can even construct rather generalized operating procedures for decision making. The military "estimate of the situation"—a checklist of things to consider in analysing a military decision problem—is an example of such an operating procedure.

There is nothing wrong with such aids to decision making except that they don't go nearly far enough. They graduate the decision maker from nursery school to kindergarten, perhaps, but they don't carry his education much further.

How then do executives discharge their responsibilities for seeing that decision making in their organizations, nonprogrammed as well as programmed, is of high quality? Let me propose an analogy. If you have a job to do, and you don't have the time or the skill to design and produce just the right tool to do it, you look around among the tools you have or can get at the hardware store and select the best one you can find. We haven't known very much about how to improve human decision-making skills, but we observe that some people have these skills much better developed than others. Hence, we rely on selection as our principal technique for improving complex decision-making skills in organizations.

Even our selection techniques are not nearly as adequate as we should like. To some limited extent we have found out how to assess human qualities by formal testing. In the main, however, we select a good decision maker for an organizational position by looking for a man who has done a pretty good job of decision making in some other organizational position that is almost equally taxing. This is a simple-minded approach to the problem, but it is the only moderately successful one that we know.

We supplement our selection techniques with two kinds of training: the professional training in basic principles that generally precedes entrance into organizational life, and the training through experience and planned job rotation that the organization itself can provide. Man is a learning animal. If he is subjected to a sequence of problem situations of progressively greater difficulty and of difficulty appropriate to the level of skill he has attained, he will usually show an increasing capacity to handle the problems well. For problems of a nonprogrammed sort neither he nor we know from whence the improvement comes. The processes of learning have been as mysterious as the processes of problem solving. But improvement there is. We are thus able, in a crude way, to use training and planned experience as a means for improving nonprogrammed decision making in organizations.

Appropriate design of the organization structure is important for nonprogrammed, as it is for programmed, decision making. An important principle of organization design that has emerged over the years has been called facetiously "Gresham's Law of Planning." It states that programmed activity tends to drive out nonprogrammed activity. If an executive has a job that involves a mixture of programmed and nonprogrammed decision-making responsibilities, the former will come to be emphasized at the expense of the latter. The organizational implication of Gresham's Law is that special provision must be made for nonprogrammed decision making by creating specific organizational responsibilities and organizational units to take care of it. The various kinds of staff units that are so characteristic of large-scale modern organizations are mostly units specialized in particular aspects of the more complex nonprogrammed decision-making tasks. Market research units and research departments, to cite some examples, specialize in the intelligence phase of decision making; planning departments and product development departments specialize in the design phase. The creation of organizational units to carry on these activities allocates brain-power to nonprogrammed thought, and provides some minimal assurance that such thought will occur in the organization.

In summary, we have not had, in the past, adequate knowledge of the processes that are involved in decision making in complex situations. Human thinking, problem solving, and learning have been mysterious processes which we have labeled but not explained. Lacking an understanding of these processes, we have had to resort to gross techniques for improving nonprogrammed decision making: selection of men who have demonstrated their capacity for it; further development of their powers through professional training and planned experience; protection of nonprogrammed activity from the pressure of repetitive activity by establishing specialized organizational units to carry it on. We cannot say that these traditional techniques have failed —decisions do get made daily in organizations. Neither can we say that we might not do very much better in the future as our knowledge of the decision-making process grows.

New Techniques for

Programmed Decision Making

Wᴏʀʟᴅ War II brought large numbers of scientists trained in the use of mathematical tools into contact for the first time with operational and managerial problems. Designers of military aircraft could not plan aircraft armament without making assumptions about the formations in which the planes would be flown and the strategy of their commitment to action. Mathematical economists responsible for material allocation had to come to grips with complex logistics systems. The need for solving these problems, coupled with the tools of quantitative analysis that the scientists and econometricians brought with them, have produced some new approaches to management decision making that are of fundamental importance.[1]

OPERATIONS RESEARCH

Many people—notably some of the pioneer operations researchers themselves—have tried to define operations research. The net result is usually to identify it with scientific method or straight thinking applied to management problems, and to imply that it is something that can be done only by natural scientists. Definitions of this kind, unintentionally imperialistic, raise the hackles of those identified with the earlier phrase "scientific management," who had thought that clear, scientific thinking is what they had always been doing. Except in matters of degree (e.g., the operations researchers tend to use rather high-powered mathematics), it is not clear that operations research embodies any philosophy different from that of scientific management. Charles Babbage and Frederick Taylor will have to be made, retroactively, charter members of the operations research societies.

[1] See Fig. I, p. 8, "eastern" half.

14

A more understandable and defensible definition of operations research is a sociological one. Operations research is a movement that, emerging out of the military needs of World War II, has brought the decision-making problems of management within the range of interests of large numbers of natural scientists and, particularly, of mathematicians and statisticians.[2] The operations researchers soon joined forces with mathematical economists who had come into the same area—to the mutual benefit of both groups. And by now there has been widespread fraternization between these exponents of the "new" scientific management and men trained in the earlier traditions of scientific management and industrial engineering. No meaningful line can be drawn any more to demarcate operations research from scientific management or scientific management from management science.[3]

Along with some mathematical tools, which I shall discuss presently, operations research brought into management decision making a point of view called the systems approach. The systems approach is no easier to define than operations research for it is a set of attitudes and a frame of mind rather than a definite and explicit theory. At its vaguest, it means looking at the whole problem—again, hardly a novel idea, and not always a very helpful one. Somewhat more concretely, it means designing the components of a system and making individual decisions within it in the light of the implication of these decisions for the system as a whole.[4] We now know a *little* about how this might be done:

1. Economic analysis has something to say about rational behavior in complex systems of interacting elements, and particularly about the conditions under which the choices that are optimal for subsystems will or will not be optimal for a system as a whole. Economic analysis

[2] Some standard works on operations research by leading members of the group are C. West Churchman, Russell L. Ackoff, and E. Leonard Arnoff, *Introduction to Operations Research* (New York: John Wiley & Sons, Inc., 1957); and Philip M. Morse and George E. Kimball, *Methods of Operations Research* (New York: John Wiley & Sons, Inc., 1951). The Operations Research Society of America publishes the journal *Operations Research*.

[3] The term "management science" was the trademark invented by the quantitatively oriented social scientists, primarily econometricians, who entered this area and who initially distinguished themselves from the operations researchers. The Institute of Management Sciences was organized in 1954. Its journal is the quarterly *Management Science*.

[4] See Churchman, *et al., op. cit.,* pp. 109-111.

also has a great deal to say about the price system as a possible mechanism for decentralizing decision making.[5]

2. Mathematical techniques have been developed and adapted by engineers and economists for analysing the dynamic behavior of complex systems. Under the labels of servomechanism theory and cybernetics, such techniques underwent rapid development at about the time of World War II. They have considerable usefulness in the design of dynamic systems.[6]

Systems design is such a modish, if not faddish, word at the moment that I don't want to exaggerate the amount of well-understood technique that stands behind it. Nevertheless, it is fair to say that we can approach the design and analysis of large dynamic systems today with a good deal more sophistication than we could ten years ago.

THE MATHEMATICAL TOOLS

Operations research progressed from the talking to the action stage by finding tools with which to solve concrete managerial problems. Among the tools, some of them relatively new, some of them already known to statisticians, mathematicians, or economists were linear programming, dynamic programming, game theory, and probability theory. Behind each of these formidable terms lies a mathematical model for a range of management problems. Linear programming, for example, can be used to provide a mathematical model for the operations of a gasoline refinery, or a commercial cattle-feed manufacturing operation. Dynamic programming can be used as a model for many inventory and production planning situations. Game theory models have been used to represent marketing problems. Probability models have been used in a wide variety of contexts—they have been, perhaps, the most versatile of all.

Whatever the specific mathematical tool, the general recipe for using it in management decision making is something like this:[7]

1. Construct a *mathematical model* that satisfies the conditions of

---

[5] See Tjalling C. Koopmans, ed., *Activity Analysis of Production and Allocation* (New York: John Wiley & Sons, Inc., 1951).

[6] The word cybernetics was first used by Norbert Wiener in *Cybernetics* (New York: John Wiley & Sons, Inc., 1948), p. 19. A good exposition of these techniques may be found in Arnold Tustin, *The Mechanism of Economic Systems* (Cambridge: Harvard University Press, 1953).

[7] See Churchman, *et al., op. cit.,* chap. V.

the tool to be used and which, at the same time, mirrors the important factors in the management situation to be analysed.

2. Define the *criterion function,* the measure that is to be used for comparing the relative merits of various possible courses of action.

3. Obtain *empirical estimates* of the numerical parameters in the model that specify the particular, concrete situation to which it is to be applied.

4. Carry through the mathematical process of finding the course of action which, for the specified parameter values, maximizes the criterion function.

In any decision-making situation where we apply this recipe successfully, we have, in fact, constructed a *program* for the organization's decisions. We have either annexed some decisions that had been judgmental to the area of programmed decision making,[8] or we have replaced a rule-of-thumb program with a more sophisticated program that guarantees us optimal decisions—optimal, that is, within the framework of the mathematical model.

But certain conditions must be satisfied in order to apply this recipe to a class of decision problems. First, it must be possible to define mathematical variables that represent the important aspects of the situation. In particular, a quantitative criterion function must be defined. If the problem area is so hopelessly qualitative that it cannot be described even approximately in terms of such variables, the approach fails. Second, the model will call for certain parameters of its structure to be estimated before it can be applied in a particular situation. Hence, it is necessary that there be ways of making actual numerical estimates of these parameters—of sufficient accuracy for the practical task at hand. Third, the specification of the model must fit the mathematical tools to be used. If certain kinds of nonlinearities are absolutely crucial to an accurate description of the situation, linear programming simply won't work—it is a tool adapted to mathematical systems that are, in a certain sense, linear. Fourth, the problem must be small enough that the calculations can be carried out in reasonable time and at a reasonable cost.

Some relatively simple management problems—for example, many problems of factory scheduling—turn out to be far too large for even

[8] Thus, operations research, in addition to providing techniques for programmed decisions, also expands their boundaries.

such a powerful tool as linear programming. It is easy for the operations research enthusiast to underestimate the stringency of these conditions. This leads to an ailment that might be called mathematician's aphasia. The victim abstracts the original problem until the mathematical intractabilities have been removed (and all semblance to reality lost), solves the new simplified problem, and then pretends that this was the problem he wanted to solve all along. He expects the manager to be so dazzled by the beauty of the mathematical results that he will not remember that his practical operating problem has not been handled.

It is just as easy for the traditionalist to overestimate the stringency of the conditions. For the operations research approach to work, nothing has to be exact—it just has to be close enough to give better results than could be obtained by common sense without the mathematics. Furthermore, it is dangerous to assume that something is essentially qualitative and not reducible to mathematical form until an applied mathematician has had a try at it. For example, I have often been told that "you can't place a dollar value on a lost order from inventory runout." But why, the answer goes, can't you estimate the penalty cost of taking emergency action to *avoid* losing the order —shipping, for example, by air express? Thus, many things that seem intangible can be reduced, for management decision-making purposes, to dollars and cents.

But we need not spin out these generalities. Mathematical techniques are now being applied in a large number of situations. In many of these situations, when mathematical techniques were first proposed there was much head shaking and muttering about judgment. The area of application is large. It is growing. But there is no indication that it will cover the whole of management decision making.

ENTER THE COMPUTER

It was an historical accident with large consequences that the same war which spawned operations research saw also the birth of the modern digital computer as a practical device.[9] The computer was conceived as a device for exploring by numerical analysis the proper-

[9] A general book on the history of the development of computers and on their use by management is John A. Postley, *Computers and People* (New York: McGraw-Hill Book Company, Inc., 1960).

ties of mathematical systems too large or too complex to be treated by known analytic methods. The systems of differential equations that were arising in aerodynamics, meteorology, and the design of nuclear reactors were obvious candidates for this treatment. It was soon realized that even larger problems were generated by the linear programming and dynamic programming models of management decision problems. Whatever the conceptual power of the mathematical models that have been used in operations research, their actual use in practical schemes for decision making hinged on the fortuitous arrival on the scene of the computer.

While computers were initially conceived as devices for doing arithmetic on problems that had first been cast in a mathematical form having known solution procedures, it gradually became clear that there were other ways of using them. If a model or simulation of a situation could be programmed for a computer, the behavior of the system could then be studied simply by having the computer imitate it and without solving, in the traditional sense, the mathematical equations themselves. In putting it this way, I make simulation sound like a simpler and more powerful technique than it really is. In general, we would need to simulate the behavior of the system not under a single set of conditions but over a whole range of conditions. Having simulated it, we would need some procedure for evaluating the results—for deciding whether the system behavior was satisfactory or not. Finally, before we could simulate the behavior, we would have to estimate accurately enough the structure of the system—simulation techniques do not at all reduce the burden of providing numerical estimates.

In spite of these limitations and difficulties, simulation has enabled an airline to determine how many reserve aircraft it should keep on hand, has been used to study highway congestion, has led to improvement in inventory control procedures for a huge warehousing operation, and has accomplished many other difficult tasks.

Of course, the bread-and-butter applications of computers to business decision making have had little to do with either mathematical models or simulation. They have had to do with automating a whole host of routine and repetitive data-processing activities that had for many years been highly programmed but not nearly so completely automated. Through this development, large-scale data processing is becoming a factory operation, an operation that exceeds in degree of automation all but a very few manufacturing processes.

THE REVOLUTION IN PROGRAMMED DECISION MAKING

The revolution in programmed decision making has by no means reached its limits, but we can now see its shape. The rapidity of change stems partly from the fact that there has been not a single innovation but several related innovations, all of which contribute to it.

1. The electronic computer is bringing about, with unexpected speed, a high level of automation in the routine, programmed decision making and data processing that was formerly the province of clerks.

2. The area of programmed decision making is being rapidly extended as we find ways to apply the tools of operations research to types of decisions that have up to now been regarded as judgmental—particularly, but not exclusively, middle-management decisions in the area of manufacturing and warehousing.

3. The computer has extended the capability of the mathematical techniques to problems far too large to be handled by less automatic computing devices, and has further extended the range of programmable decisions by contributing the new technique of simulation.

4. Companies are just beginning to discover ways of bringing together the first two of these developments: of combining the mathematical techniques for making decisions about aggregative middle-management variables with the data-processing techniques for implementing these decisions in detail at clerical levels.

Out of the combination of these four developments there is emerging the new picture of the data-processing factory for manufacturing, in a highly mechanized way, the organization's programmed decisions —just as the physical processing factory manufactures its products in a manner that becomes increasingly mechanized. The automated factory of the future will operate on the basis of programmed decisions produced in the automated office beside it.

Heuristic

Problem Solving[1]

However significant the techniques for programmed decision making that have emerged over the last decade, and however great the progress in reducing to sophisticated programs some areas that had previously been unprogrammed, these developments still leave untouched a major part of managerial decision-making activity. Many, perhaps most, of the problems that have to be handled at middle and high levels in management have not been made amenable to mathematical treatment, and probably never will.

But that is not the whole story. There is now good reason to believe that the processes of nonprogrammed decision making will soon undergo as fundamental a revolution as the one which is currently transforming programmed decision making in business organizations. Basic discoveries have been made about the nature of human problem solving. While these discoveries are still at the stage of fundamental research, the first potentialities for business application are beginning to emerge.[2] We may expect this second revolution to follow the first one, with a lag of ten to twenty years.

There are several conceivable ways in which the limitations of the new approaches to programmed decision making might be transcended.

[1] This chapter is based mainly on research on complex information processing sponsored by the Graduate School of Industrial Administration at Carnegie Institute of Technology and by The RAND Corporation, in which I have been engaged with my colleagues, Allen Newell and J. C. Shaw. Most of the ideas in it are our joint product. See Newell, Shaw, and Simon, "The Elements of a Theory of Human Problem Solving," *Psychological Review,* vol. 65, March 1958, pp. 151-166; Newell, Shaw, and Simon, "A General Problem Solving Program for a Computer," *Computers and Automation,* vol. 8, July 1959, pp. 10-17; and Newell and Simon, "Heuristic Problem Solving," *Operations Research,* vol. 6, January-February 1958, pp. 1-10, and *ibid.,* May-June 1958, pp. 449-450.

[2] See Fig. I, p. 8, "southeast" quadrant.

One of these would be to discover how to increase substantially the problem-solving capabilities of humans in nonprogrammed situations. Another way would be to discover how to use computers to aid humans in problem solving without first reducing the problems to mathematical or numerical form. Both of these possibilities hinge on our deepening our understanding of human problem-solving processes. If we understand how something is accomplished, and the processes that are involved, we can either try to improve those processes or find alternatives to them. Of course, we might invent synthetic processes without understanding how the natural process works. Airplanes were invented before we understood the flight of birds. And linear programming was applied to refinery scheduling before we knew how humans had scheduled refineries. Nevertheless, when we run out of ideas for handling poorly structured problem-solving tasks, it seems plausible to examine more closely the processes used by humans who have handled such tasks—not always efficiently, to be sure—for several millennia.

UNDERSTANDING HUMAN PROBLEM-SOLVING PROCESSES

But how shall we gain an understanding of the processes that humans use in problem solving and nonprogrammed decision making? We have been trying to explain these processes for many years. If we examine the result of these efforts, as Johnson[3] does in his survey of research on problem solving, we get the impression that they are still a far way off from explanation.

Some things have been known, however, about problem solving, both from psychological research and from common sense observation of what goes on around us (and in our own heads, too), for a very long time. We know, for example, that problem solving involves a great deal of search activity of one sort or another, that it often uses abstraction and imagery, that small hints can have dramatic effects on the ease of solution of a problem, and so on. But all the processes observed in problem solving—particularly the search activities and the use of relatively obvious perceptual clues—appear so simple that we do not believe they can account for the impressive outcomes. The achievements of the problem-solving process—the bridges it

[3] D. M. Johnson, *The Psychology of Thought and Judgment* (New York: Harper & Brothers, 1955).

designs, the organizations it builds and maintains, the laws of nature it discovers, have an impressiveness all out of proportion to the groping, almost random, processes that we observe in the problem solver at work. Little wonder that we invent terms like "intuition," "insight," and "judgment," and invest them with the mystery of the whole process.

In the psychological laboratory, we give a subject a problem—say, proving a theorem in Euclidean geometry—and ask him to think aloud while he solves it. We have no illusion that all his thought processes will rise to the level of consciousness or be verbalized, but we hope to get some clues about the course his thought takes. We tape record what he says during the ten or fifteen minutes he works on the problem.[4]

From the tape recording, we observe that the subject compares the theorem to be proved with some theorems he knows—he looks for similarities and differences. These suggest subproblems, whose solution may contribute to the solution of the main problem: "I have to prove two triangles congruent. Are any pairs of sides equal? Can I prove some pairs of sides equal?" Subproblems may, in turn, generate new subproblems, until he comes to a problem he can solve directly. Then he climbs back up to the next level of problems above. He gradually begins to assemble results that look as though they will contribute to the solution of the whole problem. He persists as he gets warmer, backs off to another direction of search when he finds a particular trail getting cooler.

At one level, nothing seems complicated here—nothing is very different from the white rat sniffing his way through a maze. But still the feeling persists that we are seeing only the superficial parts of the process—that there is a vast iceberg underneath, concealed from our view and from the consciousness of the subject.

Perhaps this feeling of mystery is an illusion. Perhaps the subconscious parts of the process are no different in kind from the parts we observe. Perhaps the complexity of the problem-solving process that makes its outcome so impressive is a complexity assembled out

---

[4] Allen Newell and Herbert A. Simon, "Simulation of Human Thought," forthcoming in *Proceedings of the Conference on Current Trends in Psychology,* University of Pittsburgh, 1959.

of relatively simple interactions among a large number of extremely simple basic elements.

Even if we find such a hypothesis appealing, how would we go about testing it? If we could construct a synthetic thought process and show that, step by step, it matched every element in the verbalized part of the human thought process—noticed the same clues in the situation, generated the same subproblems, drew from memory the same theorems—we would be justified in concluding that we understood what was going on in the human process.

The actual synthesis of thinking processes that parallel closely some thinking processes of human subjects has in fact been achieved within the past five years. The range of problem-solving tasks that has been studied in this way is still extremely narrow. However, little doubt remains that, in this range at least, we know what some of the principal processes of human thinking are, and how these processes are organized in problem-solving programs.

THE SIMULATION OF HUMAN THOUGHT

Since the work I am describing makes important use of digital computers and of some of the central concepts associated with the invention of computers, I shall have to insert here a few explanatory remarks about these devices.

The two most important general remarks are these:

1. There is nothing about a computer that limits its symbol-manipulating capacities to numerical symbols; computers are quite as capable of manipulating words as numbers.

2. In principle, the potentialities of a computer for flexible and adaptive cognitive response to a task environment are no narrower and no wider than the potentialities of a human. By in principle, I mean that the computer hardware contains these potentialities, although at present we know only imperfectly how to evoke them, and we do not yet know if they are equivalent to the human capacities in speed or memory size.

Nonnumerical Symbol Manipulation.

Historically, computers were devised to do arithmetic rapidly. Certain of their components are specially adapted to this purpose. This does not mean, however, that computers can process only numerical information. All general purpose computers have the capacities to manipulate symbols, numerical or literal, in all the ways in which symbols have to be manipulated in order for them to stand for either numbers or words. Computers can read symbols from external media, copy symbols from one internal location to another, print symbols externally, compare pairs of symbols for identity or difference, associate one symbol with another, find a symbol associated with another in memory, and erase symbols. Complex information processing, including problem solving and decision making, can be done with just such symbol manipulations as these. Nothing more is needed.

Flexible and Adaptive Response.

"But after all," the questioner always says, "how can a computer be insightful or creative? It can only do what you program it to do." This statement—that computers can do only what they are programmed to do—is intuitively obvious, indubitably true, and supports none of the implications that are commonly drawn from it.

A human being can think, learn, and create because the program his biological endowment gives him, together with the changes in that program produced by interaction with his environment after birth, enables him to think, learn, and create. If a computer thinks, learns, creates, it will be by virtue of a program that endows it with these capacities. Clearly this will not be a program—any more than the human's is—that calls for highly stereotyped and repetitive behavior independent of the stimuli coming from the environment and the task to be completed. It will be a program that makes the system's behavior highly conditional on the task environment—on the task goals and on the clues extracted from the environment that indicate whether progress is being made toward those goals. It will be a program that analyzes, by some means, its own performance, diagnoses its failures, and makes changes that enhance its future effectiveness. It is a simple question of fact whether a computer program can be written that will have these properties. And the answer to this question of fact is that such programs have been written.

I can now, in summary, state the central hypothesis of the theory of problem solving I am proposing: In solving problems, human thinking is governed by programs that organize myriads of simple information processes—or symbol manipulating processes if you like —into orderly, complex sequences that are responsive to and adaptive to the task environment and the clues that are extracted from that environment as the sequences unfold. Since programs of the same kind can be written for computers, these programs can be used to describe and simulate human thinking. In doing so, we are not asserting that there is any resemblance between the neurology of the human and the hardware of the computer. They are grossly different. However, at the level of detail represented by elementary information processes, programs can be written to describe human symbol manipulation, and these programs can be used to induce a computer to simulate the human process.

I apologize for this long methodological digression, but it is essential for an understanding of the research I shall describe that we all start from the same underlying assumptions about the nature of computers and about the nature of the phenomena we are trying to explain.

A GENERAL PROBLEM-SOLVING PROGRAM

Computer programs have been written that enable computers to discover proofs for theorems in logic and geometry, to play chess, to design motors, to improve their skills at some of these tasks, to compose music. Some of these programs are aimed at detailed simulation of human processes—hence, at understanding problem solving —others are aimed at finding ways, humanoid or not, of doing the tasks well. From almost all of them, whether intended as simulations or not, we learn something about human problem solving, thinking, and learning.

The first thing we learn—and the evidence for this is by now quite substantial—is that we can explain these human processes *without* postulating mechanisms at subconscious levels that are different from those that are partly conscious and partly verbalized. The hunch that was stated earlier is correct: Much of the iceberg is, indeed, below the surface, but its concealed bulk is made of the same kind of ice as the part we can see. The processes of problem solving are the familiar processes of noticing, searching, modifying the search direction on the basis of clues. The same elementary symbol-manipulating processes that participate in these functions are also sufficient for such problem-solving techniques as abstracting and using imagery. The secret of problem solving is that there is no secret. It is accomplished through complex structures of familiar simple elements. The proof is that we can simulate it, using no more than those simple elements as the building blocks of our programs.

From the standpoint of human simulation, perhaps the most interesting program of this kind is one labeled GPS (General Problem Solver).[5] It is called GPS not because it can solve any kind of problem—it cannot—but because the program itself makes no specific reference to the subject matter of the problem. GPS is a program that can reason in terms of means and ends about any problem that is stated in a certain general form. Let me sketch out the general idea:

Suppose that we are camping in the woods and decide that we need a table. How do we solve the problem of providing ourselves with one? We state the problem: we *need* a flat horizontal wooden surface; we *have* all sorts of trees around us and some tools. We ask: What is the *difference* between what we need and what we have? Trees are large, vertical, cylinders of wood attached to the ground; a table top is a smaller, horizontal, movable slab of wood. Hence, there are differences in detachability, size, flatness, and so on between what we have and what we need. We ask: What tools do we have to *reduce* these differences—for example, to detach the tree from its roots? We have axes. So we apply an ax to a tree and we have solved the first subproblem—to change an object rooted in the soil into an object detached from the soil.

I have, of course, vastly oversimplified the matter, but the main outlines are clear. Problem solving proceeds by erecting goals, detecting differences between present situation and goal, finding in memory or by search tools or processes that are relevant to reducing differences of these particular kinds, and applying these tools or processes. Each problem generates subproblems until we find a subproblem we can solve—for which we already have a program stored in memory. We proceed until, by successive solution of such subproblems, we eventually achieve our over-all goal—or give up.

[5] For a fuller description of the General Problem Solver, which was developed by the Carnegie-RAND research group, see the second reference cited in footnote 1 of this chapter.

The General Problem Solver mirrors this process as follows. Its programs enable it to formulate and attack three kinds of goals:

1. *Transform* goals: Change *a* into *b*.

2. *Reduce difference* goals: Eliminate or reduce the difference between *a* and *b*.

3. *Apply operator* goals: Apply the program (or operator or method) *Q* to the situation *a*.

With each of these types of goals is associated one or more methods for accomplishing it. When the goal is formulated by GPS, these methods are evoked from memory and tried. A method, for example, for changing *a* into *b* is to find a difference, *d,* between them and formulate the Reduce Difference goal of eliminating this difference. A method for reducing a difference between *a* and *b* is to find an operator that is relevant for removing differences of the kind in question, and to apply that operator. A method for applying an operator is to compare the actual situation with the situation that would make it possible to apply the operator, and to formulate the goal of changing the actual situation into the required situation.

These three goal types and the methods associated with them were not manufactured out of whole cloth. They were discovered by detailed, painstaking analysis of tape recordings of the thinking-aloud protocols of subjects who were solving problems in the laboratory. With one important exception, almost all the goals these subjects stated in the course of their efforts at solving the problems, and almost all the methods they applied appear to fit the categories I have just described. The number of protocols that has been examined is small—about two dozen, and only two or three of these in real detail. We have had only a half dozen subjects in the laboratory. Hence, I should not like to overgeneralize the data. Nevertheless, it is a fact of some interest that this body of data we have examined can be explained in terms of this small kit of problem-solving tools.

In describing GPS, I have omitted one important additional method for achieving Transform goals that was used by our subjects, and that was particularly prominent in the thinking processes of the more skillful subjects. This is a method, which we call *planning,* for transforming one object into another. It works as follows: If the goal is to transform *a* into *b,* abstract *a* and *b,* eliminating most of their detail and creating the new objects ("abstractions," "images," "models") a' and b'. Now formulate the goal of transforming a' into b'. If an appropriate kind of abstraction has been used—if irrelevant detail has been discarded, and the essential aspects of the situation retained, the new problem will generally be far easier to solve than the original one. Once it has been solved, it provides a series of trail markers to guide the solution of the original unabstracted problem. We were able to determine from the protocols the process of abstraction our subjects used, and to incorporate the planning method as one of the methods available to GPS.

Let me summarize: GPS is a program—initially inferred from the protocols of human subjects solving problems in the laboratory, and subsequently coded for computer simulation—for reasoning in terms of ends and means, in terms of goals and subgoals, about problematic situations. It is subject matter free in the sense that it is applicable to any problem that can be cast into an appropriate general form (e.g., as a problem of transforming one object into another by the application of operators). It appears to reproduce most of the processes that are observable in the behavior of the laboratory subjects and to explain the organization of those processes. On the basis of hand simulation (it has not yet run on the computer in its present general form), we can say that GPS is a substantially correct theory of the problem-solving process as it occurs under these particular laboratory conditions. How general it is remains to be seen.

GPS does succeed in capturing some aspects of problem solving that have always been thought to be part of its mystery. For example, we can show by comparison with the human protocols that sudden insight of the "Eureka!" type sometimes takes place at the moment at which the subject successfully applies the planning method and obtains a plan to guide his detailed solution. At such moments, subjects make such statements as "Aha! I think I've got it. Just let me work it out now." The planning method also gives us a basis for exploring the processes of abstraction and mental imagery, which turn out, in this case at least, to involve quite simple and understandable information processes.

SOME OTHER HEURISTIC PROGRAMS

Programs which, like GPS, carry out complex information processes by using the same kind of selectivity in exploration, the same sorts of rules of thumb as are used by humans, are coming to be called *heuristic* programs. I am afraid that I would not be much more successful in providing you with a precise definition of that phrase than I was with the phrase operations research. Heuristic programming represents a point of view in the design of programs for complex information processing tasks. This point of view is that the programs should not be limited to numerical processes, or even to orderly systematic non-numerical algorithms of the kinds familiar from the more traditional uses of computers, but that ideas should be borrowed also from the less systematic, more selective, processes that humans use in handling those many problems that have not been reduced to algorithm. It is a necessary point of view if the goal of the program writing is to simulate human thinking. It may turn out to be a useful point of view if the goal of the program writing is to supplement natural intelligence with artificial intelligence in management decision making—to bring in the computer as a problem-solving aide to the manager.

GPS is not the only program that has been written which simulates some aspects of human thinking. Space does not permit me, however, to describe any of the others in as much detail. I will limit myself to some comments on particular interesting features that one or another of these programs exhibit.

The Geometry Theorist

Gelernter and Rochester, at IBM, have written a program for proving theorems in Euclidean geometry that uses the diagram of the geometrical figure as a guide to its solutions.[6] If it notices, for example, that two angles in the diagram are in fact approximately equal, it can use this observation for generating the subproblem of proving the two angles equal.

The Checker Player

Arthur Samuel, at IBM, has written an effective checker-playing program that is capable of beating strong players.[7] The program does

[6] H. L. Gelernter and N. Rochester, "Intelligent Behavior in Problem-Solving Machines," *IBM Journal of Research and Development,* vol. 2, no. 4 (October 1958), pp. 336-345.

[7] A. L. Samuel, "Some Studies in Machine Learning, Using the Game of Checkers," *IBM Journal of Research and Development,* vol. 3, no. 3 (July 1959), pp. 210-229.

not mirror, however, the processes used by human checker players. Its most interesting aspect, for our purposes, is that it can improve its play by means of two learning routines that change its behavior on the basis of experience. One of these routines remembers past positions and their outcomes, the other modifies the function that is used for evaluating positions. Samuel has shown that these two programs produce extremely rapid improvement in play, much more than an equivalent amount of experience would produce in a human player.

Another Learning Program

The checker player is not the only learner among existing computer programs. The Logic Theorist,[8] a predecessor of GPS, incorporated several learning processes. The Logic Theorist discovers proofs for theorems in logic. It can remember proofs (and reproduce them if the same problem is posed a second time); remember theorems, and use them in proving subsequent theorems; examine its methods on the basis of its experience with them; and modify them in certain ways. When the learning procedures were introduced into the program, they produced large changes in LT's response to successive problem situations.

Chess Programs

There are now three computer programs for playing chess, one of them developed by our Carnegie-RAND research group, the others by Los Alamos and IBM, respectively.[9] None of them is a close simulation of human chess playing. The Carnegie-RAND program, however, parallels in an interesting respect the structure of the decision-making process that I outlined earlier. There I distinguished three phases of decision making: intelligence, design, and choice—processes for scanning the environment to see what matters require decision, processes for developing and examining possible courses of action, and processes for choosing among courses of action.

The chess program has similar structure although the design and

---

[8] Newell, Shaw, and Simon, "Empirical Explorations of the Logic Theory Machine: a Case Study in Heuristic," *Proceedings* of the Western Joint Computer Conference, February 1957 (San Francisco: Institute of Radio Engineers, 1957), pp. 218-230.

[9] Newell, Shaw, and Simon, "Chess Playing Programs and the Problem of Complexity," *IBM Journal of Research and Development,* vol. 2, no. 4 (October 1958), pp. 320-335.

choice phases are somewhat interwoven. The program is organized in terms of major goals, ordered by importance and priority, such as winning pieces and avoiding loss of pieces, securing control of the center of the board, developing pieces, and so on. In the first, or intelligence, stage, the chess position is examined to see what features it has that call for attention in terms of these goals. What enemy pieces can be captured? What of my own pieces are in danger of capture? And so on. The next phase, generating possible moves, arises out of the features that are discovered in the intelligence phase. For example, if a piece is in danger, moves are generated that will defend it, or remove it, or counterattack. Then the consequences of these moves are evaluated, and this evaluation provides the basis for the final stage —choice of the move that is best from among those that have been examined.

The chess program is organized in this way for the same reason that decision making is organized this way in everyday life. The chess board, though a microcosm, is exceedingly complicated. It has more features than can possibly be attended to—by man or machine— within the time available for a move. Hence, a preliminary survey that identifies the crucial features of the board that should be attended to, at the expense of ignoring others, is an essential part of an effective program.

These examples will provide some indication of how far research has progressed in explaining, through computer simulation, the heuristic processes that humans use in their nonprogrammed problem-solving and decision-making activity. Clearly, we have much to learn, still, about these processes. But much also has been explained, and the research potentialities of computer simulation techniques, which have been the chief means of producing this progress, have only begun to be exploited. Extrapolating the recent rapid gains that have been made, we can forecast with some confidence that a decade hence we shall have a reasonably comprehensive theoretical understanding of the processes of human problem solving. If we achieve this, what will be the consequences?

THE AUTOMATION OF NONPROGRAMMED DECISION MAKING

Success in simulating human problem solving can have two kinds of consequences: It may lead to the automation of some organizational problem-solving tasks; it may also provide us with means for improving substantially the effectiveness of humans in performing such tasks. Let us consider these two possibilities and their inter-relations.

If I am right in my optimistic prediction that we are rapidly dissolving the mysteries that surround nonprogrammed decision making, then the question of how far that decision making shall be automated ceases to be a technological question and becomes an economic question. Technologically, it is today feasible to get all our energy directly from the sun, and to be entirely independent of oil, coal, or nuclear fuels. Economically, of course, it is not feasible at all. The capital investment required for direct conversion of the sun's rays to heat is so large that only in a few desert climates is the process even marginally efficient.

Similarly, the fact that a computer can do something a man can do does not mean that we will employ the computer instead of the man. Computers are today demonstrably more economical than men for most large-scale arithmetic computations. In most business data-processing tasks they are somewhere near the breakeven point—whether they can prove themselves in terms of costs depends on the volume of work and on the biases of the man who makes the calculations. As chess players, they are exceedingly expensive (quite apart from the low quality of their play at the present time).

To put the matter crudely, if a computer rents for $10,000 a month, we can not afford to use it for nonprogrammed decision making unless its output of such decisions is equivalent to that of ten men at middle-management levels. Our experience to date—which is admittedly slight—suggests that computers do not have anything like the comparative advantage in efficiency over humans in the area of heuristic problem solving that they have in arithmetic and scientific computing.

There is little point in a further listing of pros and cons. As computer design evolves and as the science of programming continues to develop, the economics of heuristic problem solving by computer will change rapidly. As it changes, we shall have to reassess continually our estimates as to which tasks are better automated and which tasks are better put in the hands—and heads—of the human members of organizations. About the only conclusion we can state with certainty is that the boundary between man and computer in data processing work has moved considerably in the past five years, and will almost surely continue to move.

IMPROVING HUMAN DECISION MAKING

We should allow neither our anxiety nor our fascination to capture all our attention for the developments in automation arising from our growing knowledge of the problem-solving process. At least as important are the possibilities that are opened up for improving substantially human problem-solving, thinking, and decision-making activity.

This will not be the first time that the human species has made innovations that greatly improved its own thinking processes. One such innovation was the discovery of writing—the greatest importance of which lay perhaps in the aid it gave to immediate memory in performing tasks like multiplying numbers together. (Put away your pencil and scratch pad and proceed to try to multiply two four-digit numbers.) A second such innovation was the discovery of the Arabic number system with its zero and positional notation. A third such innovation was the invention of analytic geometry and the calculus which permitted problems of scientific theory to be considered and solved that were literally unthinkable without these tools.

All of these aids to human thinking, and many others, were devised without understanding the process they aided—the thought process itself. The prospect before us now is that we shall understand that process. We shall be able to diagnose with great accuracy the difficulties of a specific problem solver or decision maker in a specific domain, and we shall be able to help him modify his problem-solving strategies in specific ways. We shall be able to specify exactly what it is that a man has to learn about a particular subject—what he has to notice, how he has to proceed—in order to solve effectively problems that relate to that subject.

We have no experience yet that would allow us to judge what improvement in human decision making we might expect from the application of this new and growing knowledge about thought processes to the practice of teaching, and supervision, and to the design of organizations. Nonetheless, we have reason, I think, to be sanguine at the prospect.

Organizational Design:

Man-Machine Systems

for Decision Making

WITH operations research and electronic data processing we have acquired the technical capacity to automate programmed decision making and to bring into the programmed area some important classes of decisions that were formerly unprogrammed. Important innovations in decision-making processes in business are already resulting from these discoveries.

With heuristic programming, we are acquiring the technical capacity to automate nonprogrammed decision making. The next two decades will see changes in business decision making and business organization that will stem from this second phase in the revolution of our information technology. I should like now to explore, briefly, what the world of business will look like as these changes occur.[1]

Not all or, perhaps, most of the changes we may anticipate have to do with automation. As I pointed out earlier, the advance we may expect in the effectiveness of human decision-making processes is equally significant. Nevertheless, there has been so much public discussion about the automation and mechanization of data processing that I feel obliged to make some preliminary comments on this topic.

---

[1] See H. J. Leavitt and T. L. Whisler, "Management in the 1980's," *Harvard Business Review,* vol. 36, no. 6 (November-December 1958), pp. 41-48; and H. A. Simon, "The Corporation: Will It Be Managed by Machines?" paper prepared for *Management and Corporations, 1985,* tenth anniversary symposium, Graduate School of Industrial Administration, Carnegie Institute of Technology, April 21, 1960 (in press).

SOME COMMENTS ON AUTOMATION

Although we always acknowledge our debt to machinery for the high productivity of Western industrial society, we almost always accompany that acknowledgment with warnings and head shakings about the unfortunate side effects that industrialization brings. Our concern about mechanization focuses on two points in particular: the hazard it creates of large-scale unemployment, and its supposed tendency to routinize work, draining it of the intrinsic satisfactions it might have possessed. Even management people, long accustomed to reassuring their blue-collar and clerical workers on these points, reveal exactly the same anxieties when the talk turns to the automation of decision making.

Automation and Unemployment

In public discussion the danger of worker displacement through automation has been emphasized all out of proportion to its probable importance. The level of employment in a society is not related in any direct or necessary way to the level of automation in that society. There is absolutely no evidence that a society cannot and will not consume all the goods, services, and leisure that the society can produce, provided that the social and economic institutions are even moderately well adapted to their functions of regulating production and distribution. If productivity increases especially rapidly in some sector of the economy (as, for example, productivity in agriculture has in the American economy), it may lead to significant temporary dislocation and technological unemployment of existing skills. There is no reason why the many should benefit from increases in productivity at the expense of the few who are displaced. Any society can and should devise means for eliminating most of the inequity associated with the displacement of skills.

I am aware that few societies in the past have done a good job of handling the undesirable transient effects of automation. This does not mean that it cannot be done, that we should blame our woes on automation, or that we should eschew the significant benefits resulting from productivity increases to avoid dealing with these transition problems. Fortunately, as past history shows, we will not, in fact, take the last-named course.

The Pace of Automation

How difficult it will be to take care of the transient effects of automation depends on the speed with which the automation occurs. A principal factor in regulating the rate of automation is the supply of capital for investment in the new equipment that is required. We can make a very rough estimate of what would be required for the complete automation of data processing and decision making.

Taking the respective income shares of capital and labor in total national income as the basis for our estimate, we may say that at the present time about four-fifths of the productive capacity of the American economy resides in its labor force, one-fifth in physical capital. Investment occurs at an annual rate of roughly ten per cent of the capital stock. Hence, it would take perhaps forty years—several generations—to accumulate capital equivalent in value to the capitalized value of the labor force.

If automated data-processing and decision-making devices just reached the break-even point where they were competitive with non-mechanized human data processing and decision making, it would still take several generations to bring about enough investment in the new automated systems to double the per capita productivity of the economy. Moreover, a 25 per cent increase in the technological efficiency of the *human* data processors and decision makers would produce as large an increase in productivity as this total investment in automated procedures.

I don't want to put more weight on these sorts of "iffy" estimates than they will bear. Consideration of the quantities involved may have a useful sobering influence, however, on our prophecies of Utopia or of doom.

The Composition of the Labor Force

We shall assume, then, that automation may affect the complexion of the labor force, but will not affect the employment level—except that general high incomes may lead to an increase in voluntary leisure. The division of labor between man and automatic devices will be determined by the doctrine of comparative advantage: those tasks in which machines have *relatively* the greatest advantage in productivity over men will be automated; those tasks in which machines have relatively the least advantage will remain manual.

I have done some armchair analysis of what this proposition means for predictions of the occupational profile twenty years hence. I do not have time to report this analysis in detail here, but I can summarize my conclusions briefly. Technologically, as I have argued earlier, machines will be capable, within twenty years, of doing any work that a man can do. Economically, men will retain their greatest comparative advantage in jobs that require flexible manipulation of those parts of the environment that are relatively rough—some forms of manual work, control of some kinds of machinery (e.g., operating earth-moving equipment), some kinds of nonprogrammed problem solving, and some kinds of service activities where face-to-face human interaction is of the essence. Man will be somewhat less involved in performing the day-to-day work of the organization, and somewhat more involved in maintaining the system that performs the work.[2]

The Routinization of Work

We do not need to debate whether work was more creative and more enjoyable before the Industrial Revolution or after. A more fruitful question is whether the kinds of automation that are going on now in factories and in offices tend to increase or decrease work satisfactions, tend to enrich or impoverish the lives of the people who are employed there.

There are now in print some half-dozen studies that cast some light on the question.[3] The conclusion I have reached upon examining these is that there is no uniform tendency of mechanization or automation to make factory and office work either more routine or less

[2] What little evidence we have on recent factory automation suggests that it does not greatly change the distribution of skill levels. My own estimate is that the same will prove true of the automation of clerical and managerial work. This is so basically because humans will retain their comparative advantage in tasks that match their skills and abilities. Man will be, as always, the measure of what man can do relatively well. See H. A. Simon, "The Corporation," *supra,* and H. A. Simon, *Models of Man* (New York: John Wiley & Sons, Inc., 1957), chap. 12, "Productivity and Urban Rural Population Balance."

[3] Two good references are James R. Bright, *Automation and Management* (Boston: Graduate School of Business Administration, Harvard University, 1958), and S. Lilley, *Automation and Social Progress* (New York: International Publishers, 1957).

routine. The introduction of the assembly line was generally an influence in the direction of routinization. But as the level of factory automation has risen—especially the automation of repetitive manipulative tasks—automation has probably tended to make work less, rather than more, routine, and has loosened the linkage between the pace of the man and the pace of the machine.

How do these generalizations, based largely on observations of factory automation, apply to the automation of data-processing tasks? I have already essayed an answer in the previous section: Men will retain their greatest comparative advantage in jobs that require flexible manipulation of those parts of the environment that are relatively rough. Applied to the present issue, this means, I think, that automation will result in somewhat less routine or at least less repetitiveness in the work of the inhabitants of clerical offices and executive suites.

Implicit in virtually all discussions of routine is the assumption that any increase in the routinization of work decreases work satisfaction and impairs the growth and self-realization of the worker. Not only is this assumption unbuttressed by empirical evidence, but casual observation of the world about us suggests that it is false. I mentioned earlier Gresham's Law of Planning—that routine drives out nonprogrammed activity. A completely unstructured situation, to which one can apply only the most general problem-solving skills, without specific rules or direction, is, if prolonged, painful for most people. Routine is a welcome refuge from the trackless forests of unfamiliar problem spaces.[4]

The work on curiosity of Berlyne[5] and others suggests that some kind of principle of moderation applies. People (and rats) find the most interest in situations that are neither completely strange nor entirely known—where there is novelty to be explored, but where similarities and programs remembered from past experience help guide the exploration. Nor does creativity flourish in completely unstructured situations. The almost unanimous testimony of creative artists and scientists is that the first task is to impose limits on the situation if the limits are not already given. The pleasure that the good pro-

4 See James G. March and Herbert A. Simon, *Organizations* (New York: John Wiley & Sons, Inc., 1958), p. 185.

5 D. E. Berlyne, "A Theory of Human Curiosity," *British Journal of Psychology*, vol. 45 (1954), pp. 180-191.

fessional experiences in his work is not simply a pleasure in handling difficult matters; it is a pleasure in using skillfully a well-stocked kit of well-designed tools to handle problems that are comprehensible in their deep structure but unfamiliar in their detail.

We must be cautious, then, in inferring, because managerial work will be more highly programmed in the future than it has been in the past—as it almost certainly will—that it will thereby be less satisfying or less creative.

SOME FUNDAMENTALS OF ORGANIZATIONAL DESIGN

An organization can be pictured as a three-layered cake. In the bottom layer, we have the basic work processes—in the case of a manufacturing organization, the processes that procure raw materials, manufacture the physical product, warehouse it, and ship it. In the middle layer, we have the programmed decision-making processes, the processes that govern the day-to-day operation of the manufacturing and distribution system. In the top layer, we have the nonprogrammed decision-making processes, the processes that are required to design and redesign the entire system, to provide it with its basic goals and objectives, and to monitor its performance.

Automation of data processing and decision making will not change this fundamental three-part structure. It may, by bringing about a more explicit formal description of the entire system, make the relations among the parts clear and more explicit.

The Hierarchical Structure of Organizations[6]

Large organizations are almost universally hierarchical in structure. That is to say, they are divided into units which are subdivided into smaller units, which are, in turn, subdivided, and so on. They are also generally hierarchical in imposing on this system of successive partitionings a pyramidal authority structure. However, for the moment, I should like to consider the departmentalization rather than the authority structure.

Hierarchical subdivision is not a characteristic that is peculiar to human organizations. It is common to virtually all complex systems of which we have knowledge.

Complex biological organisms are made up of subsystems—diges-

---

[6] The speculations of the following paragraphs are products of my joint work over recent years with Allen Newell.

tive, circulatory, and so on. These subsystems are composed of organs, organs of tissues, tissues of cells. The cell is, in turn, a hierarchically organized unit, with nucleus, cell wall, cytoplasm, and other subparts.

The complex systems of chemistry and physics reveal the same picture of wheels within wheels within wheels. A protein molecule—one of the organismic building blocks—is constructed out of simpler structures, the amino acids. The simplest molecules are composed of atoms, the atoms of so-called elementary particles. Even in cosmological structures, we find the same hierarchical pattern: galaxies, planetary systems, stars, and planets.

The near universality of hierarchy in the composition of complex systems suggests that there is something fundamental in this structural principle that goes beyond the peculiarities of human organization. I can suggest at least two reasons why complex systems should generally be hierarchical:

1. *Among possible systems of a given size and complexity, hierarchical systems, composed of subsystems, are the most likely to appear through evolutionary processes.* A metaphor will show why this is so. Suppose we have two watchmakers, each of whom is assembling watches of ten thousand parts. The watchmakers are interrupted, from time to time by the telephone, and have to put down their work. Now watchmaker A finds that whenever he lays down a partially completed watch, it falls apart again, and when he returns to it, he has to start reassembling it from the beginning. Watchmaker B, however, has designed his watches in such a way that each watch is composed of ten subassemblies of one thousand parts each, the subassemblies being themselves stable components. The major subassemblies are composed, in turn, of ten stable subassemblies of one hundred parts each, and so on. Clearly, if interruptions are at all frequent, watchmaker B will assemble a great many watches before watchmaker A is able to complete a single one.

2. *Among systems of a given size and complexity, hierarchical systems require much less information transmission among their parts than do other types of systems.* As was pointed out many years ago, as the number of members of an organization grows, the number of *pairs* of members grows with the square (and the number of possible subsets of members even more rapidly). If each member, in order to act effectively, has to know in detail what each other member is

doing, the total amount of information that has to be transmitted in the organization will grow at least proportionately with the square of its size. If the organization is subdivided into units, it may be possible to arrange matters so that an individual needs detailed information only about the behavior of individuals in his own unit, and aggregative summary information about average behavior in other units. If this is so, and if the organization continues to subdivide into suborganizations by cell division as it grows in size, keeping the size of the lowest level subdivisions constant, the total amount of information that has to be transmitted will grow only slightly more than proportionately with size.

These two statements are, of course, only the grossest sorts of generalization. They would have to be modified in detail before they could be applied to specific organizational situations. They do provide, however, strong reasons for believing that almost any system of sufficient complexity would have to have the rooms-within-rooms structure that we observe in actual human organizations. The reasons for hierarchy go far beyond the need for unity of command or other considerations relating to authority.

The conclusion I draw from this analysis is that the automation of decision making, irrespective of how far it goes and in what directions it proceeds, is unlikely to obliterate the basically hierarchical structure of organizations. The decision-making process will still call for departmentalization and sub-departmentalization of responsibilities. There is some support for this prediction in the last decade's experience with computer programming. Whenever highly complex programs have been written—whether for scientific computing, business data processing, or heuristic problem solving—they have always turned out to have a clear-cut hierarchical structure. The over-all program is always subdivided into subprograms. In programs of any great complexity, the subprograms are further subdivided, and so on. Moreover, in some general sense, the higher level programs control or govern the behavior of the lower level programs, so that we find among these programs relations of authority among routines that are not dissimilar to those we are familiar with in human organizations.[7]

[7] The exercise of authority by computer programs over others is not usually accompanied by affect. Routines do not resent or resist accepting orders from other routines.

Since organizations are systems of behavior designed to enable humans and their machines to accomplish goals, organizational form must be a joint function of human characteristics and the nature of the task environment. It must reflect the capabilities and limitations of the people and tools that are to carry out the tasks. It must reflect the resistance and ductility of the materials to which the people and tools apply themselves. What I have been asserting, then, in the preceding paragraphs is that one of the near universal aspects of organizational form, hierarchy, reflects no very specific properties of man, but a very general one. An organization will tend to assume hierarchical form whenever the task environment is complex relative to the problem-solving and communicating powers of the organization members and their tools. Hierarchy is the adaptive form for finite intelligence to assume in the face of complexity.

The organizations of the future, then, will be hierarchies, no matter what the exact division of labor between men and computers. This is not to say that there will be no important differences between present and future organizations. Two points, in particular, will have to be reexamined at each stage of automation:

1. What are the optimal sizes of the building blocks in the hierarchy? Will they become larger or smaller? This is the question of centralization and decentralization.

2. What will be the relations among the building blocks? In particular, how far will traditional authority and accountability relations persist, and how far will they be modified? What will be the effect of automation upon subgoal formation and subgoal identification?

Size of the Building Blocks: Centralization and Decentralization

One of the major contemporary issues in organization design is the question of how centralized or decentralized the decision-making process will be—how much of the decision making should be done by the executives of the larger units, and how much should be delegated to lower levels. But centralizing and decentralizing are not genuine alternatives for organizing. The question is not whether we shall decentralize, but how far we shall decentralize. What we seek, again, is a golden mean: we want to find the proper level in the organization hierarchy—neither too high nor too low—for each important class of decisions.

Over the past twenty or more years there has been a movement toward decentralization in large American business organizations. This movement has probably been a sound development, but it does *not* signify that more decentralization is at all times and under all circumstances a good thing. It signifies that at a particular time in history, many American firms, which had experienced almost continuous long-term growth and diversification, discovered that they could operate more effectively if they brought together all the activities relating to individual products or groups of similar products and decentralized a great deal of decision making to the departments handling these products or product groups. At the very time this process was taking place there were many cross-currents of centralization in the same companies—centralization, for example, of industrial relations activities. There is no contradiction here. Different decisions need to be made in different organizational locations, and the best location for a class of decisions may change as circumstances change.

There are usually two pressures toward greater decentralization in a business organization. First, it may help bring the profit motive to bear on a larger group of executives by allowing profit goals to be established for individual subdivisions of the company. Second, it may simplify the decision-making process by separating out groups of related activities—production, engineering, marketing, and finance for particular products—and allowing decisions to be taken on these matters within the relevant organizational subdivisions. Advantages can be realized in either of these ways only if the units to which decision is delegated are natural subdivisions—if, in fact, the actions taken in one of them do not affect in too much detail or too strongly what happens in the others. Hierarchy always implies intrinsically some measure of decentralization. It always involves a balancing of the cost savings through direct local action against the losses through ignoring indirect consequences for the whole organization.

Organizational form, I said earlier, must be a joint function of the characteristics of humans and their tools and the nature of the task environment. When one or the other of these changes significantly, we may expect concurrent modifications to be required in organizational structure—for example, in the amount of centralization or decentralization that is desirable.

When the cable and the wireless were added to the world's techniques of communication, the organization of every nation's foreign office changed. The ambassador and minister who had exercised broad, discretionary decision-making functions in the previous decentralized system, were now brought under much closer central control. The balance between the costs in time and money of communication with the center, and the advantages of coordination by the center had been radically altered.

The automation of important parts of business data-processing and decision-making activity, and the trend toward a much higher degree of structuring and programming of even the nonautomated part will radically alter the balance of advantage between centralization and decentralization. The main issue is not the economies of scale—not the question of whether a given data-processing job can better be done by one large computer at a central location or a number of smaller ones, geographically or departmentally decentralized. Rather, the main issue is how we shall take advantage of the greater analytic capacity, the larger ability to take into account the interrelations of things, that the new developments in decision making give us. A second issue is how we shall deal with the technological fact that the processing of information within a coordinated computing system is orders of magnitude faster than the input-output rates at which we can communicate from one such system to another, particularly where human links are involved.

Let us consider the first issue: the capacity of the decision-making system to handle intricate interrelations in a complex system. In many factories today, the extent to which the schedules of one department are coordinated in detail with the schedules of a second department, consuming, say, part of the output of the first, is limited by the computational complexity of the scheduling problem. Often the best we can do is to set up a reasonable scheduling scheme for each department and put a sizeable buffer inventory of semi-finished product between them to prevent fluctuations in the operation of the first from interfering with the operation of the second. We accept the cost of holding the inventory to avoid the cost of taking account of detailed scheduling interactions.

We pay large inventory costs, also, to permit factory and sales managements to make decisions in semi-independence of each other. The factory often stocks finished products so that it can deliver on demand to sales warehouses; the warehouses stock the same product so that the factory will have time to manufacture a new batch after an order is placed. Often, too, manufacturing and sales departments make their decisions on the basis of independent forecasts of orders.

With the development of operations research techniques for determining optimal production rates and inventory levels, and with the development of the technical means to maintain and adjust the data that are required, large savings are attainable through inventory reductions and the smoothing of production operations, but at the cost of centralizing to a greater extent than in the past the factory scheduling and warehouse ordering decisions. Since the source of the savings is in the coordination of the decisions, centralization is unavoidable if the savings are to be secured.

The mismatch—unlikely to be removed in the near future—between the kinds of records that humans produce readily and read readily and the kinds that automatic devices produce and read readily is a second technological factor pushing in the direction of centralization. Since processing steps in an automated data-processing system are executed in a thousandth or even millionth of a second, the whole system must be organized on a flow basis with infrequent intervention from outside. Intervention will take more and more the form of designing the system itself—programming—and less and less the form of participating in its minute-by-minute operation. Moreover, the parts of the system must mesh. Hence, the design of decision-making and data-processing systems will tend to be a relatively centralized function. It will be a little like ship design. There is no use in one group of experts producing the design for the hull, another the design for the power plant, a third the plans for the passenger quarters, and so on, unless great pains are taken at each step to see that all these parts will fit into a seaworthy ship.

It may be objected that the question of motivation has been overlooked in this whole discussion. If decision making is centralized how can the middle-level executive be induced to work hard and effectively? First, we should observe that the principle of decentralized profit-and-loss accounting has never been carried much below the level of product-group departments and cannot, in fact, be applied successfully to fragmented segments of highly interdependent activities. Second, we may question whether the conditions under which middle-management has in the past exercised its decision-making prerogatives were actually good conditions from a motivational standpoint.

Most existing decentralized organization structures have at least three weaknesses in motivating middle-management executives effectively. First, they encourage the formation of and loyalty to subgoals that are only partly parallel with the goals of the organization. Second, they require so much nonprogrammed problem solving in a setting of confusion that they do not provide the satisfactions which, we argued earlier, are valued by the true professional. Third, they realize none of the advantages, which by hindsight we find we have often gained in factory automation, of substituting machine-paced (or better, system-paced) for man-paced operation of the system.[8]

The question of motivation we have just raised has a broader relevance than the issue of decentralization and I will discuss it later, in the section on authority and responsibility relations. Meanwhile, we can summarize the present discussion by saying that the new developments in decision making will tend to induce more centralization in decision-making activities at middle-management levels.

Authority and Responsibility

Let me draw a sketch of the factory manager's job today. How far it is a caricature, and how far a reasonably accurate portrait, I shall let you decide. What is the factory manager's authority? He can hire and fire. He can determine what shall be produced in his factory and how much. He can make minor improvements in equipment and recommend major ones. In doing all of these things, he is subject to all kinds of constraints and evaluations imposed by the rest of the organization. Moreover, the connection between what he decides and what actually happens in the factory is often highly tenuous. He proposes, and a complex administrative system disposes.

For what is the factory manager held accountable? He must keep his costs within the standards of the budget. He must not run out of

[8] The general decline in the use of piece-rates is associated with the gradual spread of machine-paced operations through the factory with the advance of automation. In evaluating the human consequences of this development, we should not accept uncritically the common stereotypes that were incorporated so effectively in Charlie Chaplin's *Modern Times*. Frederick Taylor's sophisticated understanding of the relations between incentives and pace, expressed, for example, in his story of the pig-iron handler, is worth pondering.

items that are ordered. If he does, he must produce them in great haste. He must keep his inventory down. His men must not have accidents. And so on.

Subject to this whole range of conflicting pressures, controlling a complex system whose responses to instructions is often erratic and unpredictable, the environment of the typical middle-management executive—of which the factory manager is just one example—is not the kind of environment a psychologist would design to produce high motivation. The manager responds in understandable ways. He transmits to his subordinates the pressures imposed by his superiors—he becomes a work pusher, seeking to motivate by creating for his subordinates the same environment of pressure and constraint that he experiences. He and his subordinates become expediters, dealing with the pressure that is felt at the moment by getting out a particular order, fixing a particular disabled machine, following up a particular tardy supplier.

I do not want to elaborate the picture further. The important point is that the task of middle managers today is very much taken up with pace setting, with work pushing, and with expediting. As the automation and rationalization of the decision-making process progress, these aspects of the managerial job are likely to recede in importance.

If a couple of terms are desired to characterize the direction of change we may expect in the manager's job, I would propose rationalization and impersonalization. In terms of subjective feel the manager will find himself dealing more than in the past with a well-structured system whose problems have to be diagnosed and corrected objectively and analytically, and less with unpredictable and sometimes recalcitrant people who have to be persuaded, prodded, rewarded, and cajoled. For some managers, important satisfactions derived in the past from interpersonal relations with others will be lost. For other managers, important satisfactions from a feeling of the adequacy of professional skills will be gained.

My guess, and it is only a guess, is that the gains in satisfaction from the change will overbalance the losses. I have two reasons for making this guess: first, because this seems to be the general experience in factory automation as it affects supervisors and managers; second, because the kinds of interpersonal relations called for in the new environment seem to me generally less frustrating and more wholesome than many of those we encounter in present-day supervisory relations. Man does not generally work well with his fellow man in relations saturated with authority and dependence, with control and subordination, even though these have been the predominant human relations in the past. He works much better when he is teamed with his fellow man in coping with an objective, understandable, external environment. That will be more and more his situation as the new techniques of decision making come into wide use.

A FINAL SKETCH OF THE NEW ORGANIZATION

Perhaps in the preceding paragraphs I have yielded to the temptation to paint a Utopian picture of the organization that the new decision-making techniques will create. If so, I have done so from an urge to calm the anxieties that are so often and so unnecessarily aroused by the stereotype of the robot. These anxieties are unnecessary because the existence in the world today of machines that think, and of theories that explain the processes of human thinking, subtracts not an inch, not a hair, from the stature of man. Man is always vulnerable when he rests his case for his worth and dignity on how he differs from the rest of the world, or on the special place he has in God's scheme or nature's. Man must rest his case on what he is. This is in no way changed when electronic systems can duplicate some of his functions or when some of the mystery of his processes of thought is taken away.

The changes I am predicting for the decision-making processes in organizations do not mean that workers and executives will find the organizations they will work in strange and unfamiliar. In concluding, I should like to emphasize the aspects in which the new organizations will much resemble those we know now.

1. Organizations will still be constructed in three layers; an underlying system of physical production and distribution processes, a layer of programmed (and probably largely automated) decision processes for governing the routine day-to-day operation of the physical system, and a layer of nonprogrammed decision processes (carried out in a man-machine system) for monitoring the first-level processes, redesigning them, and changing parameter values.

2. Organizations will still be hierarchical in form. The organization

will be divided into major subparts, each of these into parts, and so on, in familiar forms of departmentalization. The exact bases for drawing departmental lines may change somewhat. Product divisions may become even more important than they are today, while the sharp lines of demarcation among purchasing, manufacturing, engineering, and sales are likely to fade.

But there is a more fundamental way in which the organizations of the future will appear to those in them very much like the organizations of today. Man is a problem-solving, skill-using, social animal. Once he has satisfied his hunger, two main kinds of experiences are significant to him. One of his deepest needs is to apply his skills, whatever they be, to challenging tasks—to feel the exhilaration of the well-struck ball or the well-solved problem. The other need is to find meaningful and warm relations with a few other human beings— to love and be loved, to share experience, to respect and be respected, to work in common tasks.

Particular characteristics of the physical environment and the task environment are significant to man only as they affect these needs. The scientist satisfies them in one environment, the artist in another; but they are the same needs. A good business novel or business biography is not about business. It is about love, hate, pride, craftsmanship, jealousy, comradeship, ambition, pleasure. These have been, and will continue to be man's central concerns.

The automation and rationalization of decision making will, to be sure, alter the climate of organizations in ways important to these human concerns. I have indicated what some of the changes may be. On balance, they seem to me changes that will make it easier rather than harder for the executive's daily work to be a significant and satisfying part of his life.